G000124118

Key Stage 2

Using Materials

Penny Johnson

Name Brendan

Schofield & Sims

Introduction

There are lots of materials all around us. Some materials are hard and some are soft, some are see-through and some are waterproof. Some materials are found naturally and others have to be made. In this book you will learn about different materials, their properties and how to find the best material for a particular job. You will find out about materials that exist as solids, liquids and gases, as well as the processes that create natural materials such as rocks and fossils.

How to use this book

Before you start using this book, write your name in the box on the first page.

Then decide how to begin. If you want a complete course on using materials, you should work right through the book from beginning to end. Another way to use the book is to dip into it when you want to find out about a particular topic. The Contents page or the Index at the back of the book will help you to find the pages you need.

Whichever way you choose, don't try to do too much at once – it's better to work through the book in short bursts.

When you have found the topic you want to study, look out for the icons below, which mark different parts of the text.

Finally, use the Scientific investigation table on page 30 to find out how the **Understanding Science** series can help you use your new skills to investigate scientific questions in other topics.

Activities

These are the activities that you should complete. Write your answers in the spaces provided. After you have worked through all the activities on the page, turn to pages 31–35 at the end of the book to check your answers. When you are sure that you understand the topic, put a tick in the box beside it on the Contents page.

Explanation

This text explains the topic and gives examples. Read it before you start the activities. Any words shown like **this** appear in the combined Index and glossary. Turn to page 36 to see what these words mean.

Information

This text gives you useful background information and interesting facts about the subject.

Did you know?

Contents

There are two books about materials in this series: **Using Materials** (this book) and **Changing Materials**. You should work through **Using Materials** before you look at **Changing Materials**.

Materials around us

This book is made from a **material** called paper. The chair you are sitting on is probably made from wood or from metal and it may be covered with **fabric**.

The towel is made of **cotton** fabric.

The window and the vase are made of **glass**.

The outside of the plug is made of **plastic**.

The box is made of **cardboard**.

The cooking spoon is made of **wood**.

Cups and plates are made of a **ceramic** material.

The jumper is made of **wool**.

The knife is made of **metal**.

The book is made of **paper**.

The baby's cup is made of **plastic**.

The table is made of **wood**.

Properties of materials

We use different materials for different jobs because they have different **properties**. The properties of a **material** describe what it is like. The table shows some of the words we can use to describe different properties.

Property	Meaning
absorbent	soaks up water
brittle	breaks easily if you hit it
cheap	does not cost much money to buy it
flexible	bendy
hard	difficult to dent
light	easy to lift and carry
opaque	not see-through
stiff	does not bend
strong	difficult to break
transparent	see-through
waterproof	does not let water go through it

We can also use words such as soft, rough and smooth to describe what a material feels like. We usually need more than one word to describe the properties of a particular material. For example, glass is stiff, hard, transparent and brittle.

1. Write down three words to describe a ceramic material.

_____

2. Write down three words to describe wool.

_____

Comparing materials

We can compare different **materials** by thinking about their **properties**. For example, wood and metal are similar because they are both stiff and opaque. Wood and paper are similar because they are both opaque, but they are also different because wood is stiff and paper is flexible.

1. a) Write down three materials that are waterproof.

_____

_____

b) Write down three materials that are flexible.

_____

_____

2. a) Write down two ways in which metal and ceramic materials are similar.

_____

_____

b) Write down one way in which they are different.

_____

_____

3. a) Write down three ways in which glass and ceramic materials are similar.

_____

_____

b) Write down one way in which they are different.

_____

_____

Sometimes the **properties** of an object depend on its shape as well as the **material** it is made from. For example, the climbing frame shown below is strong, stiff and hard. It is made from thick metal bars.

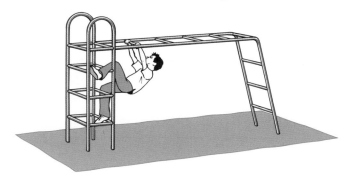

This thin metal wire is flexible and weak.

There are different kinds of plastics, so the properties of something made from plastic depend on its shape and on the kind of plastic it is made from.

This slide is made from plastic.

This drink bottle is made from plastic.

1. a) Describe the properties of the plastic used to make the slide.

_____

b) Describe the properties of the plastic used to make the bottle.

_____

2. a) Describe the properties of the wood used to make a table.

_____

b) How does the wooden table feel different from the wood used to make a fence?

_____

Choosing materials

We use a particular **material** for a job because of its **properties**, but some properties are more important than others.

For example, we use glass for windows because it is transparent and waterproof. Glass is hard and stiff and these are useful properties, but we could make windows out of a flexible material if we had to. Glass is also brittle, which is not a useful property!

1. Ceramic materials are stiff, hard, waterproof and brittle.

a) Which properties are important for making mugs and plates?

_____

b) Which property is not useful? _____

2. Why do you think that cups and plates for babies and very small children

are usually made out of plastic? _____

3. Tea towels and T-shirts are made from cotton **fabric**.

a) What is the most important property of cotton for a tea towel?

_____

b) What other property is important for tea towels?

_____

c) What is the most important property for a T-shirt?

_____

 Glass can be used to make staircases! These staircases are very expensive, because they have to be made very carefully so that the glass does not break when it is used.

Choosing materials

Sometimes we can use different **materials** for the same job.

plastic bottle

glass bottle

Many things are made from more than one material.

Polished wood looks attractive.

There is a wooden frame inside this chair. Wood is stiff, strong and cheap.

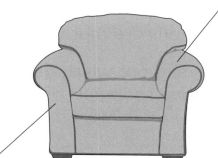

Fabric is comfortable to sit on.

4. Look at the above drinks bottles.

a) Write down one advantage of using plastic for a bottle.

_____

b) Write down one advantage of using glass.

_____

5. Mrs Patel buys a wooden table, even though it is more expensive than a plastic one. Suggest why she bought the wooden one.

_____

6. The seats in cars would be easy to keep clean if they were covered with plastic. Why do you think that car seats are usually covered with fabric instead of plastic?

_____

If you want to find the best **material** to use for a job, you may need to test some materials.

Which **fabric** is best for making a towel?

This is not a very good question, because it depends what you mean by 'best'. You could mean any of these.

- Which fabric feels softest when I dry myself with it?
- Which fabric will last the longest?
- Which fabric will soak up the most water?
- Which fabric will dry the quickest?

These questions are much better because you can investigate them scientifically.

Sarah is finding out which fabric will absorb the most water. She is going to see how many spoonfuls of water each fabric will soak up.

cotton tea towel   cotton bath towel   woollen jumper   polyester T-shirt

The pieces of material she is testing are all the same size. This is to make sure her test is fair. In a **fair test** you must only change one thing.

1. What is the one thing that Sarah is changing in her investigation?

_____

Did you know? Scientists have to make sure they carry out fair tests. They write about their investigation and show the report to other scientists so they can check that the test was fair.

Planning a test

These diagrams show some tests that are not fair.

Jack and Nia are testing **rocks** to find out which ones wear out most easily.

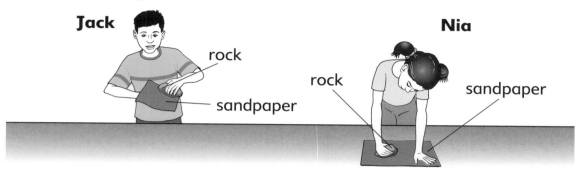

Lily and Joe are finding out which ruler is the most flexible. They make sure the weights cannot fall on their feet.

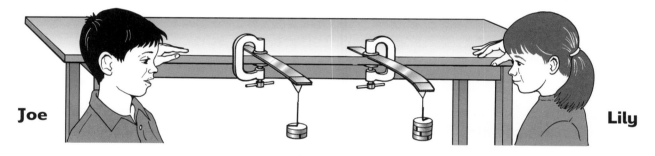

2. Why is Jack and Nia's investigation not a **fair test**?

_____

_____

3. Why is Lily and Joe's investigation not a fair test?

_____

_____

4. Max wants to find out which ball is the bounciest. He is going to drop some different balls and find out how high each one bounces.
What things will he have to keep the same to make sure his test is fair?

_____

_____

Sarah tested different types of **fabric** to see how much water they absorbed.

The cotton tea towel soaked up 5 spoonfuls. The cotton bath towel soaked up 9, the wool soaked up 11 and the polyester soaked up 3.

1. Write Sarah's results in this table. The first entry has been made for you.

Fabric	Water absorbed (spoonfuls)
cotton tea towel	5

2. Draw a bar chart to show Sarah's results. The first bar has been drawn for you.

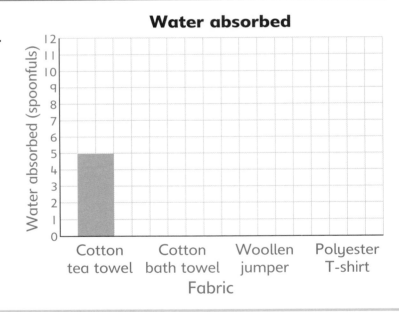

Water absorbed

A **conclusion** is when you say what you have found out in an investigation. This is Sarah's conclusion.

The wool absorbed the most water, then the cotton bath towel and the tea towel. The polyester absorbed the least water.

An **evaluation** is when you say how good your investigation was, and if you did a **fair test**. If you can, you should also say if you could make your investigation any better.

My test might not have been fair. All the pieces of **fabric** were the same size, but the wool was thicker than the bath towel and the polyester was very thin.
I could do a better test if I could find pieces of fabric that are the same thickness.

3. Lily and Joe did a fair test to find which ruler is the most flexible. The table shows their results.

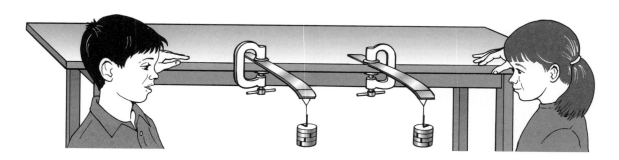

a) Draw a bar chart on the grid below to show their results.

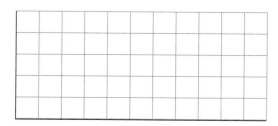

Ruler	Distance it bent (cm)
clear plastic	5
yellow plastic	2
wood	1
metal	2

b) Write a **conclusion** for the investigation. _____

_____

c) Write an evaluation. _____

_____

_____

Rocks

Rock is a **natural material**. There are rocks under the ground everywhere, but you cannot usually see them because they are covered in **soil** and plants or there are roads or buildings on top of them.

Rocks can be broken down into different sizes. Small pieces of rock are called stones, and very small pieces make gravel. Stones and gravel are used to make some buildings, paths and roads.

Rocks are made of small **grains** stuck together. The grains can be different sizes, shapes and colours. Different rocks have different kinds of grains in them, so they have different **properties**.

Rock	Description	Properties
granite	different-coloured grains with sharp edges, some grains are quite big	hard, does not wear away easily, **impermeable** (water does not run through it)
sandstone	lots of rounded grains, mostly the same size	fairly hard, can be worn away by the weather, **permeable** (because water can run through tiny gaps between the grains)
slate	tiny dark-coloured grains with sharp edges	hard rock, does not wear away easily, can be split into thin sheets, impermeable
marble	tiny grains with sharp edges, usually whitish	hard, looks attractive, does not wear away easily, impermeable

Did you know? Stones can be used to cut things. Before metal knives were invented, people used a kind of stone called flint to cut things. Flint can be broken so that it has very sharp edges.

Rocks

Jamie is testing **rocks** to find out if they are **permeable**. He puts three drops of water on each piece of rock. The diagrams show how they look after 5 minutes.

A   B   C   D

1. a) Which rock in Jamie's experiment has absorbed water? _____

b) What word is used to describe the property of allowing water to run

through a rock? _____

2. Which kinds of rock have **grains** with sharp edges?

_____

3. Which rock wears away the easiest? _____

4. These diagrams show what the grains in three different rocks look like.
Write the name of the rock under each diagram.

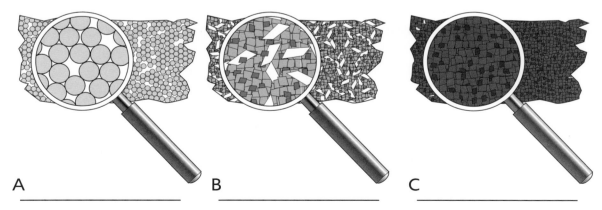

A _____ B _____ C _____

5. Rocks are chosen for their **properties**. Explain which rock you would use
for a doorstep that will have lots of people walking on it.

I would use _____ because _____

_____

Some kinds of **rock** are formed when **sediments** such as sand or mud get buried under more layers of sediment. Over millions of years the sediments turn into rocks.

When living things die, most of them get eaten or rot away. A few get trapped in sediments and their shapes can still be seen when the sediments turn into rocks. These shapes are called **fossils**.

Scientists can use fossils to find out about plants and animals that lived millions of years ago.

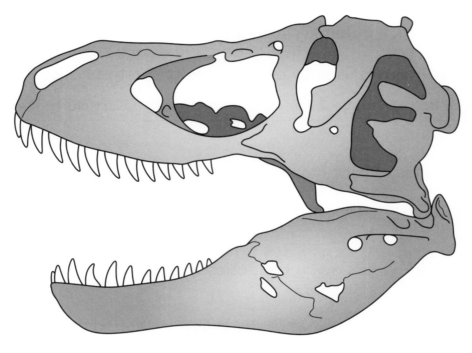

Tyrannosaurus rex was a dinosaur that lived on Earth about 66 million years ago.

1. How long does it take for sediments to turn into rocks?

_____

2. How can scientists find out about things that lived on Earth millions of years ago?

_____

Soils

Most rocks are covered in **soil** and most soils have plants growing in them. Soils are made from tiny particles of **rock** and also contain bits of **decayed** plants and animals.

Not all soils are the same. This is because they are made from the rocks beneath them and there are many different kinds of rock.

You can investigate different soils using a **sieve**. A sieve has lots of small holes in it. Small particles go through the holes, but large particles stay in the sieve.

Khalid tested some soils using two different sieves. The bar chart shows his results.

Sieve 1 (medium holes)
Large particles get trapped in the sieve.

Sieve 2 (small holes)

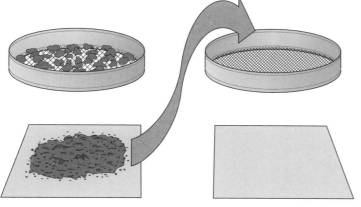

Small and medium particles fall through the sieve.

Particle types in different soils

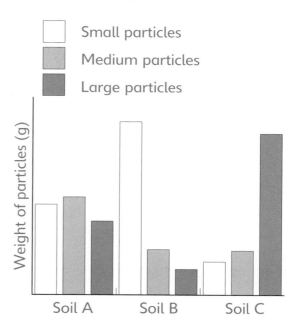

□ Small particles
▨ Medium particles
▨ Large particles

1. a) Which size particles stay in sieve 2? _____

   b) Why do these particles stay in the sieve?

   _____

2. Which soil that Khalid tested has the most large particles in it? _____

A cup of tea is hot. An ice lolly is cold. **Temperature** is a way of saying how hot or cold something is.

You can tell how hot or cold some things are by feeling them, but in science it is better to measure things if you can. You can measure temperature using a **thermometer**. The units for temperature are degrees Celsius (°C).

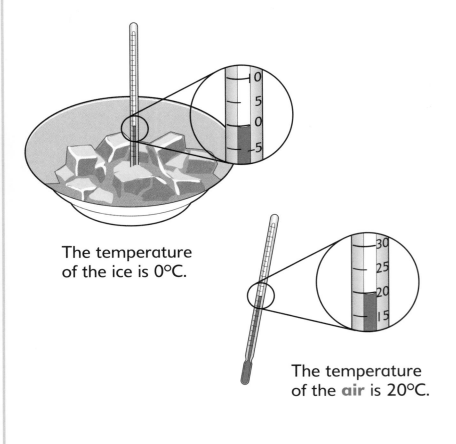

The temperature of the ice is 0°C.

The temperature of the **air** is 20°C.

The thermometer is measuring the temperature of the tea.

1. What is the temperature of the tea? _____

Did you know? The temperature of the inside of your body should be 37°C. If your body is hotter than this, you may be ill. You have a 'high temperature'.

Temperature

The **temperature** of things can change. Heat always flows from a hotter thing to a colder thing.

This tea is very hot when it is first made. It is hotter than the **air** in the room. It cools down until it is the same temperature as the air in the room. It cannot get any colder than the air in the room.

later

This glass of milk has just come out of the fridge. If you leave it out of the fridge, heat from the air will flow into the milk. The milk will warm up until it is the same temperature as the room.

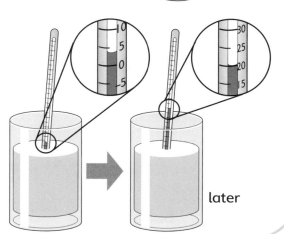

later

2. a) What is the temperature of the milk that has just come out of the fridge?

_____

b) What temperature is the milk after it has been left out? _____

3. Sam's mum takes a pizza out of the same fridge and puts it in the oven. The inside of the oven is 200°C.

a) What temperature is the pizza when it has just come out of the fridge?

_____

b) What will happen to the temperature of the pizza when it is in the oven?

_____

c) How hot will the pizza get? _____

Explain your answer. _____

Keeping things warm

The clothes you wear in winter are different from those you wear in summer. In winter you wear clothes that will keep you warm.

Amma did a test to find out which **material** was the best at keeping some water warm. She wrapped plastic cups in different materials and filled them with hot water from a tap. She measured the **temperature**, and then measured it again 10 minutes later.

I. The table shows Amma's results. Draw a bar chart on the grid below, to show these results.

Material	Temperature (°C)		
	At start	**After 10 mins**	**Drop**
bubble wrap	60	53	7
paper towel	60	49	11
cling film	60	45	15
foam rubber	60	52	8

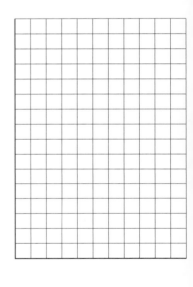

2. What did Amma have to keep the same to make sure her test was fair?

_____

_____

3. Write a **conclusion** for Amma's investigation.

_____

_____

Keeping things warm

The same **materials** that stop things cooling down too quickly can also be used to stop things warming up too quickly.

Ben wants to take some ice lollies to his friend's house. He needs to keep them cold. He puts some material inside a box and puts the lollies in the box.

4. a) Which material should Ben put in his box? _____

b) Explain why you chose this material.

_____

_____

5. Ben wants to find out if the lollies will stay colder if he uses more than one layer of material.

a) What should he keep the same to make his investigation a **fair test**?

_____

_____

b) What will he need to measure?

_____

c) What instrument will he use to make these measurements?

_____

A **material** that stops heat flowing from one thing to another is called a **thermal insulator**. ('Thermal' means 'to do with heat'.) Plastic, wood and things with trapped **air** in them (such as bubble wrap or knitted wool) are all good thermal insulators.

A material that lets heat go through it easily is called a **thermal conductor**. Metals are good thermal conductors. Materials that let heat go through them easily also let electricity go through them easily. Some metals are attracted to magnets. You will learn more about this in **Forces & Electricity**.

The pan is made of metal, so that heat from the cooker can go through it to the food.

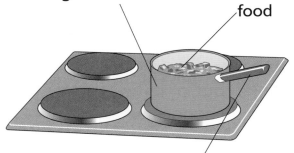

food

The handle is made of plastic, so you do not burn your hand when you pick it up.

1. How does a woolly jumper help to keep you warm in winter?

_____

2. a) What other material could be used for the handle of a saucepan?

_____

b) What property of this material is useful for a saucepan handle?

_____

3. You need to stir some very hot soup in a saucepan.

a) Would you use a metal spoon or a wooden spoon? _____

b) Explain why you chose this kind of spoon. _____

_____

Did you know? Birds fluff up their feathers when the weather is cold. This traps more air between their feathers and the trapped air helps to keep them warm.

Any **material** we find around us usually belongs in one of two groups, called solids and liquids.

A **liquid** has to be kept in a bottle or a container. Liquids flow, so you can pour a liquid out of its container. The shape of a liquid changes when you pour it into a different container, as it takes the shape of the container it is in. It is very difficult to squash a liquid. Water, honey and shampoo are all liquids.

A **solid** has a fixed shape. Things such as metal, wood and plastic are all solids. If a piece of a solid is thin enough (such as a metal wire), you can bend it or twist it to change its shape, but it does not need to be kept in a container and it does not change shape on its own. Solids can even be squashed or stretched, but this is quite difficult to do.

The shape of a liquid depends on the shape of its container.

I. Tick the correct boxes to show if these materials are solids or liquids.

Material	Solid	Liquid	Material	Solid	Liquid
wood			plastic		
lemonade			wool		
honey			paper		

2. How can you change the shape of a liquid?

_____

3. How can you change the shape of a piece of paper?

_____

Volumes

The amount of space that something takes up is called its **volume**. We need to use a measuring cylinder or measuring jug to find the volume of a **liquid**. The units for volume are millilitres (ml).

measuring cylinder

Liquids do not change volume when they change shape.

There is 200 ml of juice in this glass.

This glass is wider, so the juice is not so deep, but there is still 200 ml of juice.

1. What are the units for measuring volume? _____

2. Louise pours some water.

100 ml water

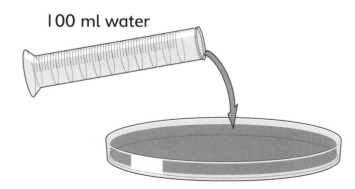

a) How much water is in the dish? _____

b) How did you work out your answer?

_____

Interesting solids

Harry is playing in the sandpit. He is pouring sand out of a bucket.

1. a) Which kind of **material** can be poured? Tick one box.

solid ☐   liquid ☐

b) Is sand a solid or a liquid? _____

Sand can flow like a **liquid** because it is made up of lots of small solid pieces. Although you can pour sand, we call it a **solid** because each piece of sand keeps its shape.

2. You can pour all the materials listed in the table below. Tick the boxes to show if each one is a solid or a liquid.

Material	Solid	Liquid
sand	✓	
water		
milk		
flour		
rice		

3. a) Suggest one way that sugar is like water.

_____

b) Suggest one way that it is not like water.

_____

Air

Air is all around us. You cannot see it, but you can feel the effect of moving air on a windy day.

Air is a mixture of different sorts of **gas**. It is difficult to investigate gases because you cannot see them.

You can show that air is real by weighing it.

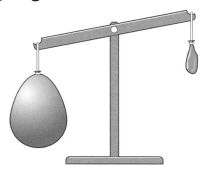

Sponges seem to have gaps in them. The gaps are full of air. If you squeeze the sponge underwater, you see lots of bubbles. The bubbles are made by the air you have squeezed out of the gaps.

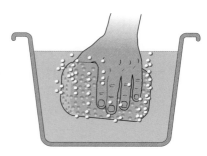

1. What kind of **material** is air? Tick one box.

   solid ☐   liquid ☐   gas ☐

2. How can you show that air is real?

   _____

3. How do you know that there is air in the gaps in a sponge?

   _____

   _____

Soil is made of lots of tiny particles. There is **air** between the particles in soils. Small animals that live in the soil need this air to live.

Not all soils are the same. Callie is investigating the amount of air in different soils.

She poured water into each soil a little bit at a time, until the soil did not soak up any more water. The table shows her results.

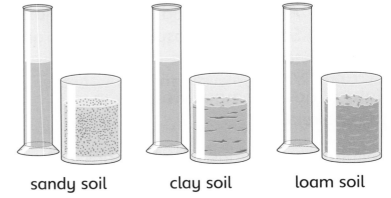

sandy soil   clay soil   loam soil

Soil	Volume of water soaked up (ml)
sandy	100
clay	20
loam	60

4. a) Which soil soaked up the most water? _____

   b) Which soil has the most air in it (before you pour water on it)?

   _____

5. What did Callie keep the same to make her test fair?

_____

Did you know? The soil under a football pitch could contain up to 10 million worms!

Different gases

There are many different **gases**. The **air** is a mixture of gases.

Oxygen is the gas in the air that we use when we breathe. All animals and plants need oxygen to stay alive. Sometimes hospital patients are given extra oxygen to breathe.

Natural gas is the gas we burn in gas cookers.

Helium is a light gas. The balloons in the picture are full of helium.

The bubbles in fizzy drinks are made by a gas called carbon dioxide.

1. Draw lines to match up the names of the gases with their uses.

Gas
carbon dioxide
natural gas
oxygen
helium

Use
breathing
bubbles in fizzy drinks
making balloons float
cooking and heating

Did you know? Packets of food are sometimes filled with a gas called nitrogen to keep them fresh for longer. The micro-organisms that make the food decay cannot grow when there is no oxygen.

A **gas** has different **properties** from a **solid** or a **liquid**.

Gases can be squashed. You cannot squash solids and liquids.

You can change the volume of gas by squashing it.

A gas spreads out to fill the container it is in. If you move some gas from a small container into a bigger one, it will spread out to fill the new container. Its **volume** has changed. Gases can flow.

1. The table summarises the properties of solids, liquids and gases. Complete the table by putting ticks or crosses in the boxes. The first row has been completed for you. (You might need to look back at page 23 to help you.)

Property	Solid	Liquid	Gas
changes shape	✗	✓	✓
flows			
keeps the same volume			
can be squashed			

2. a) Write down one way that a gas is similar to a liquid.

_____

b) Write down one way that a gas is different from a liquid.

_____

Did you know? A sponge is a solid with gaps in it. The gaps are filled with **air**. When you squeeze a sponge, you are squashing the air in the gaps. You are not squashing the solid parts of the sponge.

Scientific investigation

In this book you have found out about some of the materials in the world around you. You have learnt how to describe them and how they are used, as well as the processes that create natural materials, such as rock and fossils. You have also learnt how to ask scientific questions. Good scientists need many different skills in order to investigate things. You can learn some of the other skills you need in the other **Understanding Science** books. The table below shows you the skills you need and which books help to teach you these skills or give you practice in using them.

Skill	Book pages					
	Animals & Plants	Our Bodies	Using Materials	Changing Materials	Forces & Electricity	Light, Sound & Space
Planning an investigation						
Asking a scientific question			10		6	
Knowing what variables are	6–7			8, 22, 24		8–9, 14
Planning a fair test	6–7		10–11, 20–21	8–9	6–7, 12	8–9, 14
Predicting what you think you will find out		28–29			6–7	14
Recording and presenting your evidence						
Making tally charts		27				
Drawing pictograms		8				
Drawing bar charts		8, 27	12–13, 20	22–23, 24–25		
Drawing line graphs		28–29		10, 22–23, 24–25	17, 19	8–9
Considering your evidence and evaluating it						
Writing a conclusion	6–7	9	12–13, 20	9, 10, 25	7, 13, 17–19	
Evaluating your investigation	6–7	9, 26	13	9, 10	13, 17	15

Answers

Page 5

1. You could have written any three of these words: brittle, hard, opaque, stiff, waterproof.

2. Absorbent, flexible, light (you could also have written soft).

Page 6

1. a) You could have written down any three of these materials: wood, metal, plastic, glass, ceramic.
b) Cotton, wool, paper.

2. a) You could have written any two of these words: opaque, stiff, waterproof.
b) Ceramics are brittle (**or** metals are not brittle).

3. a) You could have written any three of these words: brittle, hard, stiff, waterproof.
b) Glass is transparent (**or** ceramics are not transparent).

Page 7

1. a) Hard, stiff, strong, smooth.
b) Flexible, light, transparent, waterproof.

2. a) Hard, stiff, strong.
b) The wood in a fence is usually rough. The wood in a table is smooth.

Pages 8 and 9

1. a) Waterproof and stiff.
b) Brittle.

2. Plastic is not brittle (**or** plastic does not break).

3. a) Absorbent.
b) Flexible.
c) Flexible (**or** soft).

4. a) It will not break if you drop it (**or** it is light).
b) It is not flexible (**or** it does not bend when you hold it).

5. The wooden one looks more attractive than the plastic one.

6. It is more comfortable to sit on fabric (**or** fabric looks more attractive than plastic).

Pages 10 and 11

1. The kind of fabric.

2. Nia is pressing harder than Jack.

3. The rulers are not sticking out by the same distance and the weights are not the same.

4. Drop each ball from the same height and drop each ball on to the same kind of surface.

Pages 12 and 13

1.

Fabric	Water absorbed (spoonfuls)
cotton tea towel	5
cotton bath towel	9
wool	11
polyester	3

2.

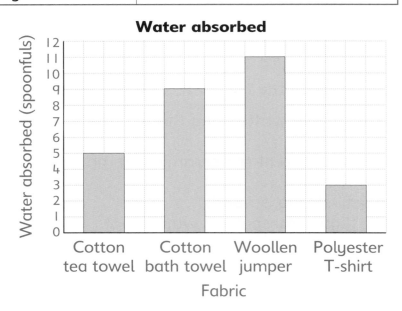

3. a)

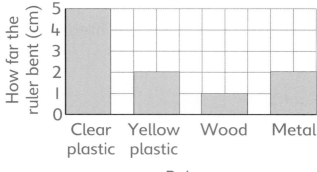

b) The clear plastic ruler bent the most and the wooden ruler bent the least.

c) The test was fair, because they used the same weights on each ruler and each ruler was sticking out by the same amount.

Page 15

1. a) A
   b) Permeable.

2. Granite, slate and marble.

3. Sandstone.

4. A is sandstone, B is granite, C is slate.

Answers

5. Granite (or slate), because it does not wear away easily (you could also have put marble, which does not wear out, but marble is too expensive to be used for things like doorsteps).

Page 16
1. Millions of years.

2. Using fossils.

Page 17
1. **a)** Medium.
   b) The holes are too small to let them go through.

2. C

Pages 18 and 19
1. 70°C

2. **a)** 4°C
   b) 20°C

3. **a)** 4°C
   b) It will get hotter (**or** the temperature will go up).
   c) 200°C. It will get as hot as the oven.

Pages 20 and 21
1.

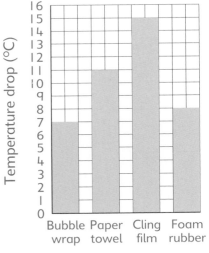

Temperature drop

2. The volume of water, the starting temperature, the thickness of the wrapping, the length of time she left each cup.

3. The bubble wrap kept the water hottest, and the cling film let the temperature go down the most.

4. **a)** Bubble wrap.
   b) It was best at keeping water hot in Amma's investigation.

5. **a)** The kind of material, the number of lollies, the starting temperature of the lollies, the length of time before he measures the temperature.
   b) The temperature of the lollies at the beginning and the temperature after the lollies have been in the box for a certain time.
   c) Thermometer (he will also need a clock to measure the time).

Answers

Page 22

1. The trapped air in it helps to stop heat from your body going through it easily.

2. **a)** Wood.
   b) It is a thermal insulator.

3. **a)** Wooden.
   b) Heat will not travel through it easily, so you will not burn your hand.

Page 23

1.

Material	Solid	Liquid	Material	Solid	Liquid
wood	✓		plastic	✓	
lemonade		✓	wool	✓	
honey		✓	paper	✓	

2. Pour it into a different container.

3. Fold it or cut it up.

Page 24

1. Millilitres (ml).

2. **a)** 100 ml
   b) It is the same amount as she had in the measuring cylinder.

Page 25

1. **a)** Liquid.
   b) Solid. (The information on page 25 will help you to understand why sand is a solid.)

2.

Material	Solid	Liquid
sand	✓	
water		✓
milk		✓
flour	✓	
rice	✓	

3. **a)** You can pour it.
   b) Sugar is made up of small pieces of solid. Water is a liquid.

Pages 26 and 27

1. Gas.

2. You can weigh it (**or** you can feel it when the wind blows).

3. You can see bubbles of air coming out if you squeeze it underwater.

4. **a)** Sandy.
   b) Sandy.

5. The amount of soil.

Answers

Page 28 **1.**

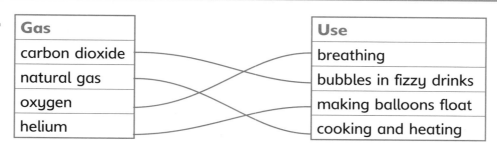

Gas		Use
carbon dioxide		breathing
natural gas		bubbles in fizzy drinks
oxygen		making balloons float
helium		cooking and heating

Page 29 **1.**

Property	Solid	Liquid	Gas
changes shape	✗	✓	✓
flows	✗	✓	✓
keeps the same volume	✓	✓	✗
can be squashed	✗	✗	✓

2. **a)** They both flow **or** they both change shape.

    b) You can squash a gas but you cannot squash a liquid.

Index and glossary